SABU THE ELEPHANT BOY

SABU
THE ELEPHANT BOY

by FRANCES FLAHERTY
and URSULA LEACOCK

LONDON: J. M. DENT & SONS LTD.

greetings to all
English boys and

girls who read
this book—from
Sabu and
Irawatha

CONTENTS

A number of photographs in this book are reproduced from the film 'Elephant Boy' by kind permission of London Film Productions Ltd.

PREFACE

THIS book is about the small Indian boy called Sabu, and of his elephant, Irawatha, who played the parts of Little Toomai and Kala Nag in the film of *The Jungle Book* story which we made in India. I thought you would like to know about Sabu himself, after, or perhaps before, seeing him on the screen. Many of the pictures you will recognize. Some are quite different ones.

While I write this Sabu is in England. One day he hopes to go back to India to Irawatha, who is still happy in his jungle life.

F. H. FLAHERTY

SABU THE ELEPHANT BOY

SABU'S home is in Mysore in India. He used to live in a little hut by a big river, in which he could bathe all the year round, because in Mysore there is no winter and the sun always shines. On each side of the river there is a jungle where there are lots of wild animals, like tigers and panthers. There are monkeys, too, which some people catch and have in their houses as pets.

Sabu's mother died when he was a very little boy, and so his father, who was a mahout (or driver), taught his elephant to rock Sabu gently in his cradle with her trunk.

When Sabu was a little older he used to go and play with the elephants while his father was out working in the jungle. This was how Sabu got to know them so well and why he is never afraid.

Sabu's father was a great mahout, and Sabu always told himself what a great mahout he would also be one day. Sabu's father's elephant was called Gudiati. She was a cow elephant and loved her mahout very much. So when one day Sabu's father died, Gudiati was very lonely. She became bad-tempered and wouldn't do anything any other mahout told her to do, so they took her away to the jungle and let her go, and eventually she died like her master.

Now that Sabu had no mother and father and no Gudiati, he also was very lonely, and he used to go down to the river to watch the other mahouts train and bathe their elephants. He used to sit there and long and long for the day when he would be a mahout with an elephant of his own.

The Maharajah, or ruler, of Mysore owned many

Sabu is never afraid

elephants, and they were kept in big elephant stables. Sabu spent a lot of his time there. There were other little boys, too, but all their fathers were mahouts and had elephants. Sabu used to feel so unhappy. He had no father and no elephant, and all the money he got was only two rupees a month. He could never buy an elephant with that unless he saved up for a very long time, and that would mean going without any food as well. It was impossible. He seemed to be taking such a long time to grow up and be old enough to be a mahout. Sabu wondered sometimes if he were going to be a little boy for ever. But still, he was really quite happy, because there were lots of exciting things happening in India all the time (though out there they seem quite ordinary). Sometimes a hungry tiger or panther would steal into the village at night, and if anybody happened to be out just at that moment the beast might attack him. But more often, somebody would see the tiger, or perhaps he would roar and then the whole village would know he was there, and they would come out and kill him or drive him away.

Sometimes a tiny snake, but one poisonous enough to kill you all the same, or even a great big snake, would creep through a crack in the wall, or through the open door, when Sabu wasn't looking, and then he would have to get a stick and beat it until it was dead.

Once Sabu was lying on the verandah of his hut when a wild elephant came out of the jungle. Sabu was all by himself except for a man some distance away, and this man did not dare come near and help him, as he was afraid that then they would both be killed. But Sabu didn't need any help, because the elephant just came up and greeted him as an old friend and they played together for over half an hour,

The river where the elephants bathed

and then the elephant went back into the jungle quite quietly, while Sabu lay down again on the verandah and went on playing by himself.

Sabu says the elephant didn't hurt him because he was wearing a talisman round his neck, which his mother had given him before she died.   She had told Sabu that so long as he wore it, no harm would come to him.

II   IRAWATHA

IN the Maharajah's stables there was an elephant called Irawatha (which means, ' The Riding Elephant of the God Indra '). He was the largest elephant in the south of India, and terribly strong.   Irawatha had been caught in the jungle by a very clever elephant hunter who was a Jemadar, or head man.

Sabu was a great friend of the Jemadar, and the Jemadar used to let him play with Irawatha as much as he liked. He was a very clever elephant and quite different from any of the others.

He had even acted differently when he had been caught. Irawatha had been a lone tusker, thrown out of his herd, because when he was younger, and not so strong, he had challenged the leader of the herd to fight, as he himself wanted to be leader.   He had lost the fight and so the rest of his herd did not want him.

Irawatha had been very lonely wandering about the jungle, as elephants like being in herds.   One day he had seen four cow elephants tethered in the forest.

' Elephants, at last ! ' thought Irawatha, and went to talk to them.

Irawatha and his mahout

He made particular friends with one cow elephant, called Pudmini, and every evening came to visit her.

One evening, however, none of the cow elephants was tethered, and they had men sitting on them, but Irawatha never noticed this ; he just went straight up to Pudmini.

She nestled up to him and another elephant came to his other side. They both began to press rather hard and flap their ears in his eyes.

' Ah ! ' thought Irawatha. ' What a handsome elephant I must be for these cow elephants to like me so much.' Irawatha never guessed that the cow elephants had been told to be nice to him, by the men.

Suddenly they left him, and he tried to follow, but something held his back leg. He looked round and saw that it was fastened by a rope tied to a tree. Now here is the queer part about Irawatha, which surprised everybody very much, because instead of losing his temper and running all over the place like other wild elephants caught in this way, Irawatha just stood still.

The men on the other elephants waited and waited for him to get cross, but he just didn't. At last the Jemadar, who was leading the elephants, went up to Irawatha on his cow elephant, and tied one of Irawatha's legs to a leg of the cow. Then he started to lead the way down to the river.

There, Irawatha had a long drink and a bathe and then went off back to the stables quite quietly with the other elephants.

Here Irawatha was different again. Instead of refusing to eat any food, or drink any water, like other wild elephants, he ate and drank and got larger and stronger. Most wild elephants die when they are captured, because they are so

Irawatha took hold of Sabu with his trunk and swung him up into the air

sad to leave the jungle, and that is why they are not caught,
unless they begin to make trouble and kill people. Wild
elephants that are roaming about the jungle alone do a lot
of damage. When they get cross from being alone too
long, they go and knock people's houses down and stop
cars on the road. They have to be killed or got rid of, then.

Now, Irawatha was a really tame elephant, and Sabu used
to teach him many tricks while they played together. One
trick, which no other elephant could do, was for Irawatha to
take hold of Sabu with his trunk and swing him up into
the air over his head and on to his back. This was a very
special and secret trick of theirs, because Sabu knew none
of the other boys could do that with their elephants. It
was useful, too, when naughty Sabu wanted to steal melons
from the roofs of the houses where they lay ripening.

One day, Sabu was having his meal with the other boys.
They were swapping their food, because Sabu liked a lot
of bananas, whilst Uday liked a lot of rice. Sabu gave his
rice to Uday, and Uday gave his bananas to Sabu.

Sabu ate his bananas, talking all the time with his mouth
full, telling the boys that as his father had been a great
mahout so he, Sabu, would be, too.

' Bah,' said the other boys. ' How can you be a great
mahout ? Why, you haven't even got an elephant.'

' Just you wait,' said Sabu. ' I'll show you I can
manage an elephant as well as you, one day.'

Just then the Jemadar came up to the boys.

' Have you heard of the white man who has just
arrived ? ' he said.

' No,' answered the boys, rather bored. White men
were always coming to see the Maharajah, but they seldom
saw the white men, or the Maharajah, for that matter.

Sabu and Irawatha stealing melons from the roofs of the houses

' Well, he's going to make a picture that moves, of a
little boy.   Here's your chance, all of you.'

A white man.   A moving picture.   A little boy.   Perhaps one of them.   What a noise the boys made, yelling
and shouting at the tops of their voices, that it was they
who would be chosen.   Sabu fell out of the party.   He
went to Irawatha.

' Oh dear, Irawatha,' said Sabu.   ' If only the white
man would choose you and me.   But he won't.   I haven't
a father or mother, and worst of all I haven't got an
elephant.'

III   SABU MEETS THE BARA SAHIB

SABU still had his two rupees a month to live on.   A rupee
in English money is about the same as one shilling and
sixpence, which doesn't sound very much, if you have to
buy all your food with it for a month ; but out in India
you can buy much more with it than you can in England.
Besides, everybody liked Sabu so much that they often
would say : ' Come, Sabu, have a meal with us.'   So you
see it was a lot to him.

When he did want to buy his own food, he would go into
the bazaar and look at all the food, turning it over and
smelling it, to make sure it was the best.   He knew which
was the best.   He knew that at so-and-so's shop, rice was
cheaper than at the shop across the way, and that on Fridays
he could get melons at a lower price than other days, because
they were rather older, but they were just as good, really,
though sometimes a bit over-ripe.

Sabu knew a shopkeeper who would give him vegetables

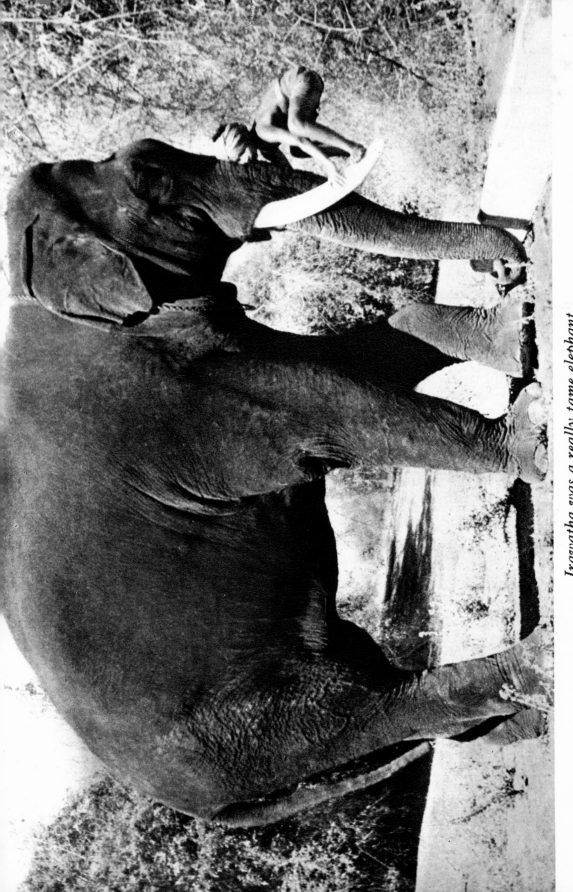

Irawatha was a really tame elephant

if he went and helped him dig his garden, and if he ran
errands for another man, he always got a sweet or two for it.

Sabu used to love to listen to the gramophone in one of
the shops. He remembered when he had first heard it.
He couldn't think how it managed to make a noise like that.
He had thought that there must be a tiny little man inside
to do it all. He remembered when once the gramophone
had gone wrong the man who owned it had taken it to bits,
whilst Sabu had told him to be careful not to let the little
man inside jump up and run away. The man had laughed
and said there was no man. Sabu didn't believe him.

It was the Maharajah who gave Sabu the rupees. The
Maharajah always helps everybody who hasn't anything
to live on. He is the father of all his people, and is a very
kind, beautiful man, who lives in a wonderful palace.
Sabu knew he was beautiful, because he had seen him ride
Irawatha, who was the Maharajah's best elephant, in
processions.

He is a very rich man. It would be nice to be a
Maharajah, Sabu used to think. He had heard people
say wonderful things about him. How he had had a very
bad elephant in his stables, so bad that the mahouts
wanted to shoot it. But the Maharajah said : ' No, let
me see this bad elephant first,' and then he went down to
the stables himself and put his two hands on the elephant's
trunk and said :

' You have been a very bad elephant, but I will forgive
you, so you must now be good.'

Then the Maharajah went away, and from then on that
elephant was a wonderful elephant and always did what it
was told.

Sabu used to wonder which elephant it had been ;

The Jemadar

certainly not Irawatha, because Irawatha had always been a good elephant and always would be, Sabu knew.

Each month Sabu would go to a house and knock on the door, and when he went inside, a man would give him his two rupees with which to buy all his food. One day, Sabu was just coming out of the house when he saw a white man. He stopped and stared. It wasn't often that he saw a white man, and the funny thing was that the white man was staring back at him.

Then suddenly the white man walked across to Sabu and said something that he didn't understand, but another Indian told him that the white man had asked him if he would like to try to be a mahout in a moving picture which a white man was going to make. Sabu's heart jumped. Had he not secretly hoped that he would be chosen? But now that he had actually been asked to take a test he could hardly believe his ears.

It was all very exciting. He had never been in a car before and here he was driving along at a terrific speed. It seemed awfully funny, after the slow movements of an elephant. He began to wonder which was best, elephants or cars, but soon decided that elephants were much nicer. After all, a car couldn't pick up a log of wood just by hearing a few words from its driver, but then on the other hand an elephant didn't always start up with just one little push of one's foot. But even so, there was no doubt about it, elephants were much better and they don't make any noise, Sabu decided hastily, as they drew up just outside a very large, white house.

Irawatha was the Maharajah's best elephant and walked in processions

SABU was not the only little Indian boy brought to
the white man who was taking the photographs for the
film.   There were five others.   They all lived together in
a tent and they played together all day, while the Bara
Sahib (which means ' big white chief ') watched them a
lot to see which was the strongest and which one would
be able to act the best.

They used to have great fun playing games and wrestling,
and they used to tease each other and play lots of practical
jokes.   There was one little boy there who was very funny.
His name was Sultan.   Sabu and Sultan got on very well
together.   To amuse the other boys sometimes, Sabu
would play on his little Indian musical instrument, while
Sultan would sing funny songs and pretend to be first a
Maharajah and then a beggar, or fat or thin, or tall or short,
and he was so funny that when the Bara Sahib and his
family watched, their sides would ache with laughing.

It took the Bara Sahib a long time to decide which was
best, though he soon noticed that in all the games Sabu
was the leader.   He told the other boys what to do and
could always climb the trees fastest.   If they were wrestling Sabu nearly always won.

One day, the Bara Sahib was just getting ready to go off
to a place called Karapur to photograph some elephants
swimming across a river that was in flood and running very
fast, when he noticed Sabu playing by himself nearby.
The Bara Sahib still says he doesn't really know why he
called to Sabu, but he just did, and asked him if he would
like to come along to Karapur with him.

Here was more excitement.   It meant another ride in

A car couldn't pick up a log of wood

the car, and Sabu thought that perhaps the Bara Sahib and the chauffeur would both go away for a minute and then he would toot the horn, and then again perhaps if they were away for a long time he could even sit in the driver's place and push down all the funny pedals and play with the sticks. None of the other boys had done that, and so he would be able to go home and tell them about it.

On the way to Karapur the car stopped twice. Sabu held his breath and wished and wished that the Bara Sahib and the chauffeur would get out of the car, but somehow they never seemed to get out at the same time. Sabu began to feel quite cross with them, but when they got to Karapur and he saw the many elephants there, waiting to cross the river, he forgot all about the car and the chauffeur and the Bara Sahib. Elephants were elephants, and much nicer than cars. He did think that it would be a good idea to buy a hooter and fix it on to the elephant, somehow, but the elephant might not like it. Still, he could try.

They all got out of the car and walked to the bank of the river. The Bara Sahib asked each of the mahouts in turn whether they would cross the river on their own elephants. But the elephants refused to go. They were afraid of the river, which was racing past. Sabu saw the Bara Sahib looking worried, so he went up to him and said that he could make Irawatha go. The Bara Sahib was not quite sure whether Sabu should go or not, but Sabu was quite sure. He could do anything with Irawatha.

I expect some of you are wondering how most Indians get on to an elephant, because you all know that an elephant is very large and very tall, and when you are at the Zoo you have to go up steps to get on top of one, before you can go for a ride. But the Indians don't need any steps. They

Sabu and Sultan playing with a native drum

either get on by making the elephant lie down, when they climb up by holding on to its tail, or they make the elephant hold up its foreleg, and climb first on to its toes and then on to its knee, and finally hold on to its ear and pull themselves on to its shoulders.

Sabu was so sure that it was safe for him to cross the river that the Bara Sahib let him go ; then he had a surprise —Sabu didn't make Irawatha lie down and climb up by his tail. He didn't make Irawatha raise his foreleg, either. The Bara Sahib wondered what Sabu was doing, standing quietly in front of the elephant. Then all of a sudden, Irawatha picked up Sabu with his trunk and put him gently on to his back. The Bara Sahib was too surprised to speak, and before he could, off set the great big Irawatha with Sabu looking even smaller than usual on his broad back behind the mahout, wading deeper and farther into the river.

Irawatha was soon out of his depth and he swam and swam as hard as he could, but the river just swept them down and down. Sabu turned as far as he dared to look back towards the party watching him anxiously. He saw them grow smaller and smaller. He looked at the opposite bank, but it seemed no nearer—he wasn't sure that it mightn't be just a very little nearer. . . . All the time he was hanging on for dear life. If he had let go for a second he would have been swept off the elephant's back, and he would have gone on down the river for many miles. He might, and might not, have been seen again, because there are lots of crocodiles in the rivers of India, and they like to eat people, if they can catch them. But they didn't catch Sabu. He held on all the time as tight as he could, and when Irawatha at last was able to swim to the bank, they

Irawatha holds out his leg for Sabu to climb up

were nearly a mile down the river from where they had started.

All this time, while Sabu was being swept away, the Bara Sahib and all the rest of the party with the cameras were very frightened. The Bara Sahib had not realized the river was running quite so fast and he was really worried. So he was tremendously relieved when he saw Sabu, far away in the distance, rise slowly out of the water on the elephant's back.

He was overjoyed and smiling all over, and he smiled still harder when at last Sabu came running up to him safe and sound. The first thing that Sabu said were three short words, and I expect that you can guess what they were—in English, at any rate.

' Will I do ? ' or in Hindustani—' *Main laiq hun ?* '

The Bara Sahib didn't need to say ' yes ' with his mouth, because he said it with every part of his face, which was one big smile. Now it was Sabu's turn to be happy. He danced up and down. Then he stopped. He took a sly look at the car. Everybody round him had stopped patting him on the back, in that queer white man's way, and were bending over black boxes on sticks, which he had been told were cameras, but every time that he had tried to touch one many warning voices commanded : ' Don't touch.' So he had given up trying to find out anything about them.

Sabu glanced at all the people and ran off to the car. In he jumped and pressed down all the pedals and punched at the round rubber thing that went toot. This was glorious ; one pedal was stiff and another easy, and a third went down and down until he couldn't reach to push it any farther. He was having the greatest fun when he heard footsteps. He looked up and saw the Bara Sahib and the chauffeur

All of a sudden, Irawatha picked up Sabu with his trunk

coming towards the car. The Bara Sahib laughed when
he saw Sabu, but the chauffeur gave him such a look.
Sabu shivered. What would happen now ? But nothing
happened except that he didn't like looking at the
chauffeur's face at all.

V   SABU LOOKS AFTER IRAWATHA

SABU and the Bara Sahib stayed at Karapur several days.
Now that Sabu had definitely been chosen to act the part
of Little Toomai in the film, he started work with Irawatha.
He loved Irawatha, and Irawatha loved his new little
master. Sabu didn't only look after Irawatha when he was
being filmed, but he also took him down to bathe in the
river every morning.

At the river's edge, Sabu would make Irawatha choose a
good stone to do the scrubbing with.

' Look, Irawatha, that one. No, not the big one. Yes,
that one. No, don't drop it, silly elephant. The one you
picked up just there. Up with it. Thank you, and now in
you go.'

And in Irawatha would go. Then Sabu would make
Irawatha lie down in the water and scrub his back hard
with the stone. He would get hold of one of Irawatha's
ears and give him a tug to make him lie on his side and
scrub that well, too. Then the other side, and his ears and
his head and his trunk.

Sabu was very thorough. He used to be very rude to
Irawatha if he didn't like his eyes washed.

' Don't be silly, you big baby ! I have to do mine with
soap. If that gets in, it stings awfully. So it just shows,

Coming out of the river

Irawatha, that even if you are older than me, you are a baby
still.   Anyway, you ought to be able to wash your own face.
I can. Look!' Then Sabu would wash his face in the
river, rubbing it twice as hard as he really did when he got
up in the morning.

If Irawatha was being lazy and wouldn't lie down, Sabu
would say to him :

'You big tub!' Sabu would put on a stern face and
talk in a voice like a school-teacher. 'Really, Irawatha,
you're the laziest elephant I've ever seen. Lie down.
Think of all the trouble I have in the morning. I have to
clean my teeth, and wash my *dhoti*,[1] and then I have to
cook my breakfast. Your breakfast comes and all you do is
eat it, and then you won't lie down in the river. Irawatha,
lie *down*.' Then Sabu would laugh and laugh. He loved
to pretend that he was somebody else and not Sabu at all.

One day Irawatha thought he would play a joke on Sabu,
so while Sabu was busy scrubbing his back, he drew a
whole lot of water up his trunk. Sabu got down from his
back to start doing his ears, but all of a sudden Irawatha
sprayed him all over with water. Sabu thought this so
funny that he rolled over and over in the water, while
Irawatha sprayed him some more. Sabu and Irawatha
were late for the filming that morning.

VI   IRAWATHA IS ILL

THE next thing to be photographed was a lot of elephants
coming over a bridge. This was a particularly hot day, and
about lunch-time, which is always the hottest part of the

---

[1] Loin cloth.

At the river's edge, Sabu would make Irawatha choose a good stone to do the scrubbing with

day, everyone was rather cross and tired because they had
to take photographs of the elephants crossing the bridge
over and over again. Each time something had gone
wrong, or else they were not quite sure that it was good
enough. Sabu was sitting on Irawatha's back singing a
song to himself. All the elephants were ready to go but
were just waiting for someone to tell them to.

Suddenly Irawatha started going forward rather fast.
Sabu stopped singing in the middle of his song and hit him
with his goad. But before he could say one sharp word,
Irawatha had given a loud snort and stuck his tusks right
into the side of the elephant in front (who was called Gunga
Prasad), and pushed him into the side of a house, which
came tumbling down. Gunga Prasad gave a loud squeal,
and everybody was very frightened, because they thought
that the elephants would all start running about and would
stamp on them. Then Sabu stuck his goad into the corner
of Irawatha's eye, which sounds nasty, but it doesn't hurt
an elephant half as much as it would hurt you or me, and
it hurt Irawatha enough to make him stand still and stop
hurting elephants and breaking things, and this made all
the other elephants stand still as well. Everybody then
began to come back, and stopped wondering which was
best : to be trampled down by elephants or to jump into the
river and perhaps get eaten by a crocodile. People came
and congratulated Sabu for stopping what might have meant
many deaths, and their hearts began to beat at a normal
speed and not with the bang, bang, bang that they had been.

Sabu was rather cross with Irawatha for hurting Gunga
Prasad, although they found that he wasn't very badly
hurt. But they had to lead him home and put him in his
stable to have a few days' rest to get better.

He would give Irawatha a tug to make him lie down

They couldn't do any more photographing that day so
they all went home. Sabu took Irawatha home too, and
all the way told him what a bad elephant he was, and that
he couldn't understand it at all. But next day everyone
understood. Irawatha had gone *musth*! When an elephant goes *musth* it means that he has a certain illness
which makes him mad for any time from two to three
weeks. Some elephants get this illness about once a year,
but no one can tell when it is going to happen, the same as
when you get measles. No one can tell that you have got it
until you come out in spots. Elephants don't get spots,
but they have a little hole in their foreheads, and from this
hole oil oozes out. They are very dangerous when they are
musth, and their mahouts tie them up twice as strongly as
they generally do, and when they give them their food they
push it to them on long sticks, so as not to come too near.
But the elephants won't eat or drink, and Sabu used to
watch Irawatha nodding his head from side to side, and
trumpeting, and looking very sick and unhappy, and that
made Sabu look very unhappy as well. What made it all
so much worse was that another elephant had to take
Irawatha's place in the film.

Sabu did not like this elephant at all. He was called
Lakshmi. Lakshmi, with the eye that squinted outwards
with a wicked gleam. Lakshmi, who would never do as
Sabu told him, because he didn't like being told what to do
by small boys. Oh! what trouble Sabu had with him.
As soon as work was over, Sabu would leave him. He
would never stay and pet him. He would not take Lakshmi
to bathe in the river and go swimming with him. Lakshmi
was a bad elephant, who would only do what his own
mahout told him to do. Sabu didn't want to do anything

Sabu washing Irawatha's big ear

with Lakshmi if he could help it ; he would much rather sit beside Irawatha.

' Irawatha, you must get better,' Sabu would say, as he watched him grow thinner and thinner. ' Look, Irawatha, I have brought you the very nicest bamboo shoots I could find. I have brought you some beautiful sugarcane. Oh, please, Irawatha, eat it, grow fat and strong again.' But Irawatha would just pick up the sugar-cane and throw it over his head. He wouldn't eat a thing.

Sometimes Sabu would sing to Irawatha. In his songs he would tell him the wonderful things that would happen to him when he got better. Irawatha would be seen all over the world in moving pictures. In places across so much water that you couldn't see the other side, even if you climbed the highest hill. The people in those places would see Irawatha upon a big white thing called a screen, doing all the wonderful, clever things he knew, and they would all love Irawatha. But Irawatha just went on nodding his head from side to side, looking very, very unhappy.

Those three weeks passed very slowly for Sabu, but at last Irawatha was better. Sabu was so happy he couldn't stand still, and spent as much time as he could petting his elephant, and giving him good food to eat. His beautiful Irawatha was now better, he was getting fat once more, and strong. No more Lakshmi, thought Sabu ; just Irawatha.

Now that Irawatha was really better, there was a scene to do for the film : of Sabu waking in the jungle with Irawatha standing over him. He has to take a piece of sugar-cane out of the *dhoti* he wore round his middle. (He kept it just stuck in the folds of this cloth because Indian boys don't have any pockets.) In the film

Sabu was sitting on Irawatha's back, singing a song to himself

he then has to begin to eat it, while Irawatha pushes his
trunk forward to have a piece too.   But Sabu won't let him
and goes on eating it himself.   Then Sabu looks up into
the trees, and sees a lot of monkeys playing there, so he
throws them a piece of sugar-cane.   But while he is watching them squabble over it, Irawatha steals the sugar-cane
and eats it before Sabu sees him, then Sabu shakes his fists,
and calls Irawatha a bad elephant.

   The first time they acted this scene, Sabu thought it was
nice ; he liked sugar-cane, and Irawatha liked it too, and so
he thought it was fun, and so did the monkeys.   When they
had done it three times, it still was nice, but when they had
done it six times, it began to get boring.   Sabu was sick of
sugar-cane by now.   When they had done it seven, eight,
nine, ten times, it was awful.   Sugar-cane was horrid stuff
now, Irawatha was tired of it, and so were the monkeys.
They kept running away and finding other things to amuse
them.   Irawatha forgot to take the sugar-cane, because he
didn't want it, and it was terribly boring.   Those poor
naughty monkeys, the forgetful Irawatha, and the sleepy
Sabu just had to go on doing it again and again, until
Sabu wondered whether Bara Sahib had gone *musth*,
because he was getting so worked up.   ' How many more
times,' thought Sabu ; ' I shall be sick soon,' and then
at last someone called out ' Cut,' and that was the end.

   ' Hurrah ! ' cried Sabu, and kicked a bundle of sugar-
cane lying near over the bank and into the river.   No more
sugar-cane for quite a bit, Sabu thought, though Irawatha
was not quite sure whether to agree or not.

   There were a lot of little scenes like that to be taken, and
Sabu and Irawatha enjoyed doing them, unless they had to
eat something over and over again.

Irawatha was trumpeting, and looking very sick and unhappy

ONE evening, after a day of hard work, Sabu joined a group of Indians, and listened to their conversation. Suddenly he started. Somebody had said ' Kheddah ! ' Sabu knew what that meant, and he began to ask a thousand questions, because a kheddah is a very exciting thing. It is when a stockade is built, and a lot of wild elephants are driven into it, so that when the gates are closed they can't get out. Sabu's father had told him all about kheddahs, and Sabu had longed to see one. They do not have kheddahs very often in Mysore, in fact only when there is a new Viceroy. (A Viceroy is an Englishman who comes to India and rules for the King. The King can't be in two places at once, and so a Viceroy has to see that orders are obeyed, and if anything serious happens, and there isn't time to ask the King what to do, the Viceroy does what he thinks is best.)

You can't have a kheddah at any time in the year, because the wild elephants are often difficult to find. The best time of the year is in March. Instead of having lots of rain as we usually do in England just then, they have day after day of hot sun in India, and everything begins to get very dry, and the places where the elephants get their water in the jungles all get dried up, just as a lot of ponds do in England in the summer-time. So the elephants have to come down to the river for their drinks and bathes. Wild elephants are very fond of water and they always bathe twice a day. But I think they do that because it makes them cool and it is so nice swimming about, more than because they like to keep clean. They also drink and drink, till you wonder how the water finds room for itself, even in an

Irawatha at last was better. But when he went out he had to be led, and you can see he has chains on his foreleg

elephant. And when you watch an elephant eat its dinner you stop wondering altogether why an elephant is so large. It eats two whole cartloads of green food every day. What a long time dinner would take if we had to eat that much. It sounds as if we would have to start at breakfast and probably not be finished until supper-time. What a day that would be.

Kheddahs have to be very carefully arranged, to be sure of capturing the elephants, and so someone has to do a tremendous lot of thinking, and it was Sabu's friend the Jemadar who did it. Every day lots of men went out into the jungle and climbed up trees and hid behind bushes, to see if they could find any elephants, and it was a week or so before they did. All the time the search was going on a big stockade had to be made. All the tame elephants were hard at work, and hundreds of men too. They had to chop down trees and drag them to the place where the stockade was going to be made, and have all the logs put in position and tightly tied. Elephants are very good for this work because they are so strong. When a tree had to be chopped down, the men would only have to chop it a little, and then an elephant would come along and give it a push with his head and over it would topple on the ground.

One day two men did as much chopping as was necessary on an extra large tree. It really was a very big one. An elephant came up and gave it a push, but the tree would not come down. He tried again and then again, but still the tree would not budge. Then another elephant tried, and another and another. The mahouts were shouting at each other ; they wanted to see whose elephant was the strongest. But none of them could push the tree down. So the two men got ready to chop it a bit more. Sabu had

Irawatha steals the sugar-cane

been watching all this time. Now he smiled and gave
Irawatha a little push, whispering in his ear, ' Go on,
Irawatha, show them what we can do, and look just as if
you were knocking a stick over.' Then he walked forward,
brushing past all the other elephants, with his nose in the
air, and pointed to the tree. Irawatha understood, and as
though it was really rather a nuisance but to please everybody he would do it, Irawatha walked slowly towards the
tree, put his head against it, and . . . pushed it right
over ! That shows you how strong he was.

Irawatha could do more than that. The logs had to
be taken to the stockade. Most of the elephants dragged
them along by chains. A few picked them up cleverly
between their tusks and trunk and carried them that way ;
but these few didn't even dare glance at the big log lying
there that Irawatha had just pushed down ; they all knew it
was far too heavy for them to carry. But Irawatha stepped
forward and, at a command given gently by Sabu, picked it
up and carried it off towards the stockade.

Before he got to the stockade, Sabu thought that he
would have some fun. He told Irawatha to put down the
log. Sabu wanted Irawatha to dance on it. He had
guessed how funny Irawatha would look, and he did too.
First Sabu made Irawatha raise one foot and then the other,
and all sorts of funny things. ' Come along, you lazy
elephant,' Sabu would shout, ' up with that leg ! ' He
pretended to be serious all the time, but inside he was
laughing like anything. Irawatha could see Sabu was
really laughing, and he decided that he would have his
laugh at Sabu some time too. But Sabu couldn't go on
having his fun for long, because he heard shouts, and saw
all the men who were building the stockade beckoning

The monkeys got tired

to him. They were in a hurry, and so Sabu made Irawatha pick up the log again and carry it the rest of the way.

Now Irawatha had to do a difficult thing that only very few elephants can do. It was to lift the gatepost of the stockade into place. A gatepost is an extra-large post about thirty feet high. If your father is six feet tall, think of him as five times higher still and you will know how tall the gatepost is. It is also wide and very strong, so that the elephants can't knock it down when they come inside the stockade. The way that the Indians put the post into place was by first digging a hole eight feet deep in the ground, and then they dragged the post up to the hole so that one end would fall into it if the gatepost stood upright. Then they fixed three very strong ropes on to the top end, and all the Indians they could find came and pulled and pulled. But the best job was done by Irawatha. He put his forehead on to the post and pushed, but he didn't only push, he had to steer it as well. The big post would start to sway to the left, and Irawatha carefully pushed it straight again, and then the post would sway the other way and again Irawatha gave it a careful push, and so it went on till the post was right in place, and didn't need any more straightening. All the time Sabu stood by Irawatha, and helped him by telling him what to do when the post began swaying badly, but even though Sabu did help him, it needed a very clever elephant to do it.

It took six whole weeks to build the stockade, and no wonder, because there were over ten thousand logs to be cut down and put in place. You will never guess how much rope it took to tie those logs together. Nine tons! That must be miles and miles. The last thing that had to be done to the stockade was to test it. They didn't want to

Even the women carried sand on their heads from the beach of the river to help build the stockade

fill it up with wild elephants if they were not sure that it was strong. So they made all the elephants come and barge themselves into the wall, and wherever it looked as though it was not strong enough, they tied it up with some more rope. Sabu thought this great fun. He nearly fell off Irawatha once, when he took a rather long run and hit the fence very hard with a bump, but he just managed to stick on. Sabu went on testing longer than he really needed to, but at last the elephants went home to bed, and the great stockade was finished.

All this time there were things happening in the jungle. The scouts had come back one evening saying that a herd of wild elephants had been seen by a little stream in a thicket of bamboo. Young bamboo shoots are elephants' favourite food, so they must have been having a lovely time. The scouts said that they seemed to be staying in the same place all the time, and everybody wondered why. Then a scout saw a big mother elephant with a tiny little baby that could only just walk. So that was the reason they kept in the same place: the whole herd had been waiting for the baby to be born and until it should be strong enough to come with them.

One day, while the stockade was still being made, the white people thought it would be fun to go and look at the herd, so they all got on elephants, and Sabu went along too, right off into the jungle. After they had been going for some time, they suddenly saw a great big tusker (that is, a father elephant) a little way in front of them. Elephants can't see very well, and they can't hear very well, but they can smell everything that is near or far away. The tusker was just standing still. Then he raised his trunk and began to sniff, sniff, sniff, all around him. Suddenly there

Irawatha at work

was a lot of squealing just behind the party, so they started
to try to get away, but on looking back they saw the
tusker slowly following.   Sabu didn't like the look of the
tusker, but all this was really rather fun and he wasn't a bit
frightened.   Then he saw that all the white people looked
whiter than ever and their eyes were very wide open.

A mother and a father sambhur with their children
suddenly crossed their path.   They are rather like deer,
and everybody seemed to look rather relieved at seeing
something that couldn't harm them.   But they soon
stiffened up again as they suddenly saw a huge cow elephant
looming up on one side.   And through the trees ahead
they saw a lot of young tuskers and they were squealing in
the way they do when they are angry.   The trees all round
began to shake, and the whole party eventually realized that
they were in the very middle of the elephant herd.   The
leaders of the party quickly whispered together, not daring
to talk aloud, and they decided to go home.   As they
turned away they saw the hind leg of the tusker disappear-
ing among the trees.   They turned away again, to one side,
because tuskers often like to hide in the jungle and then
come out again and attack you just as you are passing.
The farther away they got, the happier everyone became,
and when the camp came in sight they were very merry,
and those who had stayed at home were told exactly what
had happened, and how awfully exciting it had been.

A lot of people came up to Sabu and asked him what he
thought about the adventure.   ' Oh ! ' said Sabu, ' it was
great fun to watch the white people's faces.'

Irawatha dancing on the log

SABU wasn't always a good little boy waiting to be filmed. Sometimes he would slip off into the jungle and play games and do things by himself. One day he decided to take a holiday with Irawatha and catch a loris. Sabu had seen one in a certain tree, and he wanted it very much, because they are such funny little animals. They are like teddy-bears, with eyes as large as saucers and, like an owl, they can see at night as well as you and I can see in the daytime. They have big ears, too, and little snub noses, and every move they make is very, very slow.

The tree that Sabu had seen the loris in was very high, and had not got any branches until half-way up, but that didn't matter, because Sabu knew what he could do. He could make a ladder. If you had a good long pole and could stick big strong nails in it all the way up, like steps, you could make a ladder too. Sabu didn't have to have any nails. There was a thick clump of bamboo growing near by. He pointed out to Irawatha the strongest, tallest stalk he could see, and Irawatha put his trunk around it and began to pull. And he pulled and he pulled, and it was a good thing he was so strong. He pulled and he backed, and he backed and he pulled until the big bamboo stem came too.

Bamboo can be very tall, taller, in fact, than a lot of trees ; and it has branches sticking out on each side all the way up. Sabu cut the branches so that they were only about a foot long, and made Irawatha prop it against the tree in the right way ; but Irawatha had to hold it all the time so that it did not fall over.

Sabu ran up the bamboo like a monkey and was soon

At last the great stockade was finished

chasing the little loris through the branches. The loris
was very hard to catch, because it was much more used to
climbing trees than Sabu. Up and down and round and
about they ran. Sabu had cut off a bit of the long piece of
cloth which he wears around his head as a hat, and was
trying to catch the loris in it. It was a long time before
Sabu managed to catch it, and tie it in the piece of stuff,
and when he had, he looked down to see if Irawatha was still
holding the bamboo. But no ! Irawatha was eating grass
a few yards away.

' Hi, Irawatha, you come back here, wicked elephant,
come back here,' called Sabu, but Irawatha still remembered
when Sabu had made him dance upon a log, and he was
getting his own back. Once more Sabu shouted. ' Here,
you mountain of laziness, do as I tell you, let me get down,
you rascal. Irawatha, you old tub, come here at once, at
once, I tell you ! ' But Irawatha just tossed his trunk,
and went on eating, as though Sabu was not there. Sabu
tried another way of making Irawatha come. He didn't
want to stay up in the tree all night, so he said,

' Good, kind Irawatha, please let me down, the Bara
Sahib will be waiting for us. Please come, Irawatha, my
pearl, my king of elephants, and I'll give you a piece of
sugar-cane.' Irawatha pretended not to listen. ' Then
I'll give you a whole lot of sugar-cane,' called Sabu. Irawatha pricked up his ears, but still went on munching
grass.

' Irawatha, Irawatha, dear, good, kind Irawatha, I'll
give you a whole bunch of sugar-cane, and a beautiful ripe
melon.' Irawatha now heard. A melon. What a thought !
A nice juicy melon. Irawatha stopped eating, and looked
towards the ladder.

They all got on elephants and Sabu went too

' Irawatha, beautiful, strong Irawatha, I'll give you two melons.' That did it. Up came Irawatha. Up came the ladder swaying into place, and down came Sabu with the loris. Sabu was really rather cross with Irawatha, but all the same, Irawatha got his sugar-cane and melons that night.

IX   DRIVING THE WILD ELEPHANTS

THE elephant herd was on the same side of the river as the stockade, and it would have been impossible to drive them into it from there as the gate was facing the river. So it was decided that the best thing to do was to make them cross the river and then drive them back again over the river opposite the entrance to the stockade. An elephant looks such a big strong animal that it makes you wonder how the people managed to make the elephants cross the river at all. But they have ways of frightening the elephants and so getting them to go where they want. One is to light fires at night, because, as you know, nearly all animals are afraid of fire. In the day, as well as the night, they get lots and lots of Indians to make a circle around the herd, and shout and scream, and bang things, and shoot into the air so as not to hurt anyone, and they have rockets, little bombs, and pieces of bamboo that have a slit half way down the middle. When you wave these in the air they make a very loud clack, clack, clack. The elephants don't like this at all, and generally go away from it. But they didn't all run away in this drive across the river. Some very exciting things happened.

Sabu was riding behind the white man, Peterson, on an

They decided to go home

elephant. It wasn't Irawatha, because they didn't want to take any chance of Irawatha getting hurt. In fact, Sabu had a very difficult time persuading the white people to let him go either. But they thought him safe behind Peterson, who was a very good shot.

An elephant is one of the hardest animals to shoot, because its skin is so awfully thick, that he thinks someone has thrown a pea at him if you shoot him with a bullet. But there is a place on an elephant where you can kill him. It is just between his eyes, and a spot not more than four inches square. What sometimes happens is that when a wild elephant is charging somebody, he puts his trunk up right over those four inches, and so you can shoot as much as you like without harming the elephant.

Sabu was feeling very happy sitting on the elephant, and the white man had let him look at the gun, and had shown Sabu how it worked. But Sabu hadn't been allowed to use it, though he asked if he could. Everything was very quiet and still, except occasionally there would be a terrific banging over to the left, then silence once more. Again there was a bang, bang, bang, from the right, which soon died out. Then all of a sudden two great big cow elephants with their babies dashed through the line of beaters, who tumbled all over the place trying not to get trodden on. Out of the bushes a tusker came charging at them. He was much, much larger than the cow elephants. Peterson grabbed his rifle and fired. The tusker swayed and lurched from the shock. Peterson fired again, but just as he did so the elephant he was on swerved and the bullet went astray. Peterson's bullet had hit the tusker an inch or so too high, but the tusker was frightened and ran away. Peterson turned and saw Sabu grinning and pointing to the ground.

The loris

There sat another white man, who had been on an elephant
but had fallen off, and he had only narrowly escaped being
trodden on by the wild tusker.   He had been kicked by the
elephant Peterson and Sabu were on, but luckily he was
only a little scratched.

That spoilt the drive for that day.   If Peterson had not
been a good shot, the wild tusker would have killed the
tame elephant and his mahout.   He then would have
attacked the beaters, who weren't even on elephants.   That
shows you what brave men the beaters are, because you
never know when a tusker may turn back.

They had a difficult time getting the herd to cross the
river.   Things kept going wrong, but at last one night it
was managed, and all the beaters had to rush across too, to
surround the elephants and not let them get away.   The
circle around the elephants was very large—if you walked
all round the edge of it, you would have walked seven
miles.   Every ten yards you would have seen one of the
jungle men sitting on the ground, or collecting dry sticks for
his fire.   Perhaps if you had been there at the right moment
you would have seen him suddenly jump up and begin yelling
and screaming at the top of his voice, and rattling his stick of
bamboo, making an awful noise.   Then you would have looked
round into the jungle to see what was the matter.   At first you
probably wouldn't have seen anything, and then if you had
looked very hard you would have seen what looked like a grey
ghost, slowly moving among the trees, with hardly a sound.

So the jungle men have to have sharp ears and even
sharper eyes.   All through the day, and all through the
night, the jungle men sat by their fires, shouting and every
now and then making their hullabaloo.   Every day they
moved their fires a little farther in, making the circle smaller

Irawatha had to hold the bamboo so that it did not fall over

and smaller. The great day was coming very near now, and Sabu was getting very excited, although he was rather cross with the white men, because they wouldn't let him ride an elephant in the kheddah. They said that it was too dangerous, and Sabu rather scorned them, thinking that they were afraid, while he wasn't a bit. All he could do was to climb up in a tree, and sit there, and wait and watch.

Everything was being got ready for the final day. The men were tying the ropes just a little tighter on the stockade, to make quite sure that it was safe. Platforms on the trees were being built everywhere so that people could sit up there and watch and take photographs easily.

The evening before the final drive, great tree branches were cut down and tied to the sides of the stockade, so that the elephants would think that it was just the jungle, and not get suspicious. Elephants were led round and round the kheddah so that the smell of white people would be lost in the smell of elephants. I told you how well elephants can smell, and you see how careful one has to be.

Next morning, everybody got up very early and went to sit on their platforms in the trees. Sabu sat in his tree, looking up and down the river, wondering where the elephants would come out. By twelve o'clock in the morning, he began to get bored. This wasn't at all exciting, just sitting in a tree, looking at a river. Now and then a crocodile would slide into the river with a quiet slish . . . slosh. . . . But Sabu had seen lots and lots of crocodiles before, and so he wasn't at all interested. He watched all the white people with the cameras. They kept pointing them up and down the river. They too didn't want to miss the elephants when they came rushing out of the jungle.

Sabu and his loris

No one was allowed to talk at all and no one was allowed to smoke.   The Bara Sahib didn't like this a bit, because he smokes a great deal, and finds it hard to stop, but he was very anxious to capture the elephants. Sabu lay down on his platform. What a hot day it was. There were two birds at the top of his tree, hopping from branch to branch, and singing. This was just like any other day, hot and quiet, and the birds seemed to think so too . . . and then suddenly there was a loud bang . . . shouts and yells, clapping and shots from guns. The elephants were coming.

Sabu jumped up and looked along the river towards the noise. The camera people were all fidgety and ready to press all the buttons and turn all the handles on the cameras at once. The trumpeting of the elephants grew louder and louder. Where were they going to cross the river ? And then in a sudden hush the elephants dashed out of the jungle, plunged into the river, and were swimming down it very fast. So fast, that Sabu had only just time to gasp before they were out of sight. Sabu stood still, he was so happy all of a sudden. It had been so wonderful to watch and to hear. Sabu had often heard elephants trumpeting, but he never thought that they could make so much noise. And now everything was quiet again.

The elephants had crossed the river and had run along the bank. But they had been stopped by the tall fences leading from the stockade down to the river, and stretching a mile each way. They had turned, and then run straight into the stockade. Those poor elephants were surprised when they found the gates closed, and that they were shut in all round. The trumpeting they set up could have been heard several miles away.

The wild elephants crossing the river

The white people soon finished gasping at this sight and clambered down the trees, and they all made their way to the stockade as quickly as they could. Sabu went, too. But he didn't really like it. The elephants were so unhappy and stood there making such sad noises, and would you believe it, the cow elephants were much the bravest. They kept giving a loud trumpet and then charging against the side of the stockade, which would quiver under their weight. But the tuskers used all their weight and all their tusks in trying to get to the middle, which was farthest away from the white men. There were several young elephants, but there was one very, very tiny one, and it was getting so pushed about by all the others that everybody thought it would be killed. Sabu wanted to go in and save it, but the Jemadar, who was very brave, went in and pulled it out. What a lively little baby it was. Jumping about and playing with everybody. It was dreadfully thirsty, but it couldn't drink with its trunk yet, it was too young, and so some men held open its mouth while others poured the water in. They stopped when they thought that it had had enough, but the baby still went on trying to drink out of the puddles on the ground and from a big flat dish, which it tried to pick up with its mouth. It was very muddy and dirty, and so the Indians took it down to the river to bathe, but at first it wouldn't go in alone. It looked just as if it were saying that it wouldn't go in until mother came, and that she had told it not to. But when it at last got in, what a happy time it had. Drinking and drinking and drinking. Splashing about, rolling over and over, until when it came out it was as clean as could be.

Sabu spent a lot of time with the baby, and they played

The jungle men on platforms in the trees, looking for the wild elephants

together for hours on end. Sabu nearly forgot the film whilst he was with the baby, and he was very sad, when he heard, three days later, that the elephants were to be let out again. But he was only sad because of the baby. He was glad that the herd was to be let free.

Three o'clock on the third day was the time set for the opening of the gates. Once more everybody climbed on to their platforms to watch the rush.

The baby was let loose just in front of the stockade where the elephants, when they came rushing out, would find it. Sabu was anxious. He was afraid all those big elephants would come rushing out so fast that they would not see the little baby waiting there and would crush it. An Indian woman had poured a whole lot of water over it, because the elephants might not like the smell of the baby if she didn't. Everybody had been patting it, and wild elephants don't like the smell of humans—it frightens them. If the mother smelled the smell of all those people on her baby she might be terrified and run away and not want it again.

Sabu lay full length along a branch. A bugle sounded. That meant only fifteen more minutes until the gates would be opened. How slowly the minutes passed. He tried to count the seconds, but he had counted half an hour's worth before the second bugle sounded. The elephants came out in three lots. Sabu watched for the baby. It didn't come with the first rush. There was a pause and then the second lot came dashing out. A baby. Was it Sabu's ? No, it was a little older, and Sabu watched it plunge into the water with its mother and start bravely to swim for the other shore. Just as it reached the bank long after its mother there was a roar. Out of the stock-

The wild elephants were shut up in the stockade

ade came the rest of the elephants, with the large tuskers, one right at the back, and there was the little baby at his heels. Running, running, as fast as it could to keep up with the others, and to find its mother. The trumpeting became a roar when the elephants struck the water, and in a few seconds they were right over the river, and had disappeared into the jungle. But the baby was still only halfway across the river. Sabu clenched his fists, as he watched the poor little thing swimming in circles round and round, expecting any moment to see it drown. Someone shrieked, ' Save the baby.' Then everyone started shouting until suddenly a raft floated down towards it and towed it across the rest of the river. Everybody began to shout and cheer and wave. Sabu crossed the river and made the baby comfortable in the sand. He then said good-bye to it, while two men stayed to watch it. But early in the evening its mother came and took it away, back into the jungle.

Sabu went back across the river to bed. Yes, he had seen a kheddah at last. It had been exciting, but he was glad it was over. He was happy for those elephants back in their freedom of the jungle. Drowsily he wondered how the baby was. It would be far away now. Sabu knew the elephants would spend all the night walking, walking. Getting as far away from the place of the kheddah as possible, and he didn't blame them.

X   THE FEAST

THE jungle men had been so brave in the kheddah, and had worked so hard, that the Bara Sahib thought that it would be a nice idea to give them a feast. Sabu thought

There was one very tiny elephant

that this would be a very nice idea as well, and his eyes
shone very brightly as he watched the food coming in, and
being distributed amongst the jungle men, and he began to
breathe deep, deep breaths as he smelt the mutton being
roasted, just as I expect you do, when you peep into the
kitchen at home, and smell something nice in the oven.
The feast was held on the river-shore, which made everything look so exciting. It was not a bit like a feast in
England, where everybody sits round one table, and lots of
people serve you and give you creamy things to eat.
Instead, all the men from one village went to one place and
built a fire, and all the men from another village went and
built a fire somewhere else. As there were twelve hundred
men, and they all came from any number of different
villages, the whole shore was covered with these big fires,
on which the sheep were roasting. Besides sheep they had
all sorts of other food, rice, tea, and sugar, and food that
only Indians eat. They were very happy sitting there and
singing songs, eating and drinking until they could eat no
more. Sabu was always very popular with all the jungle
men, and he went round from group to group having a
bite of food everywhere he went until he was so full that he
could hardly walk. So he lay down for a bit near
Irawatha, and played with his trunk.

Suddenly he heard all the jungle men stirring, and begin
shouting. He got up and went over to the Bara Sahib.
But the Bara Sahib didn't notice Sabu because he was so
busy handing out medals to the men. All twelve hundred
walked past him one by one, and to each he handed a medal
which looked like a half-crown on a green piece of ribbon.
Only the half-crown had a picture of Sabu sitting on
Irawatha on one side, and a picture of a camera on the other.

The baby elephant couldn't drink with its trunk yet

The jungle men were awfully excited and very happy.
They all danced and sang ; it was not until the early hours
of the morning that they curled up in their blankets and
went to sleep.

XI   LAKSHMI

THE kheddah now over, everything went just as usual again.
There was no rush and bother, and filming went on as
before, until all of a sudden Irawatha went *musth* again.
Poor Sabu. He was always so unhappy to see Irawatha ill.
Once again he sang songs to Irawatha, picked him the
nicest bamboo shoots, and told him how he hated Lakshmi,
because now he was again riding Lakshmi. Sabu even
went as far as telling the Bara Sahib that Lakshmi was bad
and stupid. The Bara Sahib agreed that Lakshmi was
stupid, but, well, he didn't think he was bad so far ; however,
he soon saw Sabu was right.

Sabu was just giving Irawatha a lovely bamboo shoot,
trying his best to make him eat it, when he heard someone
calling him. He dropped the bamboo, and with a sad
farewell went off to find who wanted him. It was the Bara
Sahib. There was some more photographing to be done,
and Sabu was to go and tell the mahouts to bring their
elephants along. ' That means I will have to ride Lakshmi
again this morning,' thought Sabu, and he frowned very
hard, and pouted his mouth. ' At any rate,' he thought,
' I won't ride him to the place where the filming is to be
done ; his mahout must take him.' So Sabu got on another
elephant just behind Lakshmi. They all walked down the
road in single file, because otherwise if a car came along it

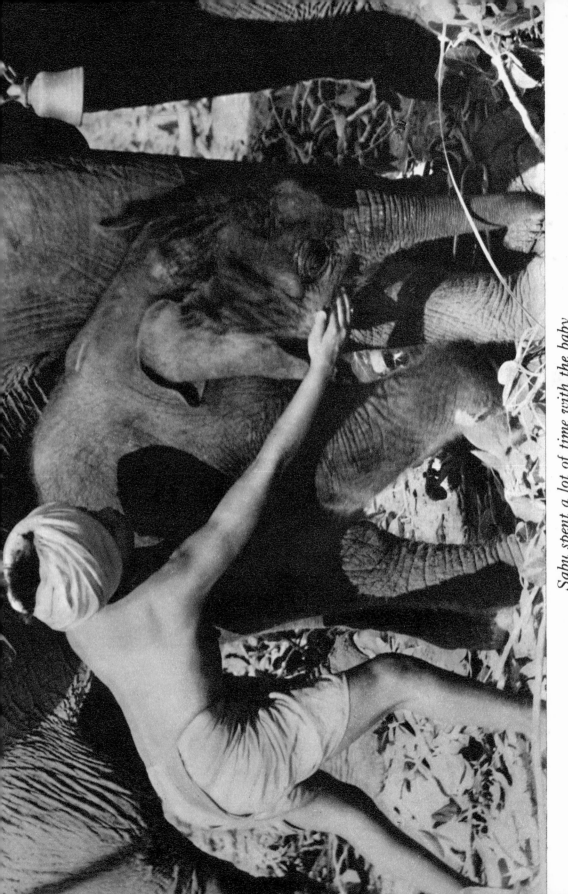

Sabu spent a lot of time with the baby

wouldn't be able to pass. Sabu kept an eye on Lakshmi,
as he always did when he was near. You never could tell
what Lakshmi might do. Lakshmi was in an awfully bad
temper that morning, making nasty grunts and waving his
trunk about in the air.

The elephant in front of Lakshmi had not got his mahout
on his back, for he was walking just behind him. 'I
wouldn't walk just in front of Lakshmi for anything,'
thought Sabu, 'not for anything at all.' Just as he was
thinking this he heard a cry. He looked down, and there
was Lakshmi with the poor mahout, who had been walking
just in front, in his trunk, beating him on the ground again
and again. Sabu just stared. He couldn't do anything to
save that poor mahout. Lakshmi, whom he had always
said was wicked, had been too quick. 'Oh! wicked
Lakshmi, I shall never ride you again. Now everyone can
see I was right. You have killed a mahout. May you die,
Lakshmi, may you die soon,' cried Sabu, though nobody
heard ; they were all too busy standing around the mahout.
Sabu slipped down from his elephant and ran off back to
the stables, back to Irawatha, and imagine his surprise,
when he saw Irawatha standing quietly, peacefully munching sugar-cane. Irawatha was better.

XII   FAREWELL

IRAWATHA and Sabu once more started work together.
Irawatha was better and Sabu didn't care about anything
else in the world. Nothing, nothing, nothing, until one
day the Bara Sahib called to him.

'Sabu,' he said. 'I've got a surprise for you.'

The mother elephant and her baby

What could it be, wondered Sabu ; is it a present or something ?

' Would you like to come to England with me ? '

Sabu sat down with a big bump, and just said, ' WHAT ? '

The Bara Sahib laughed and calmly said,

' Yes, we are packing up soon, and going back to England.'

Sabu couldn't say anything.   He just nodded his head, and stared and stared at the Bara Sahib.   Could it really be true ?   Just think of all the white people he would see there.   Everybody white, pink and white.   Whatever would the sea be like ?   Sabu had never seen the sea.   And London ?   He had heard that London was very large and he began to imagine what it would be like.   He thought it would be rather like Mysore, with its wide spacious roads, with flowers and fountains in the middle and along the sides of them.   He thought the houses would be low and flat-roofed, with stone railings carved in beautiful patterns round the top.   He thought it would be clean and the houses brightly coloured.   He thought that Buckingham Palace would have domes and minarets and would look very rich.   He thought there would be bazaars with lots and lots of little shops, like boxes, selling food and clothes and all sorts of funny things. (And that is how he went on thinking until he actually arrived in London.)

Some days later Sabu thought of something else.   Would he have to leave Irawatha behind ?   England would be lovely with Irawatha, but not without him.   This did make Sabu sad after all the excitement.   He decided to go and ask the Bara Sahib if Irawatha could come away too.   He didn't think it would be much trouble.   He would look after him himself.   No one else need bother, and so he ran off to the Bara Sahib's house.   He loved the Bara

The wild elephants were right over the river in a few seconds

Sahib's house.   It was so large, with its two big elephants'
heads carved on the gates ; but this time he didn't notice
the heads, and he didn't notice the beautiful garden, or the
gardener, who stopped digging to wonder what had gone
wrong with Sabu.   Why was he running so fast, with such
a queer look on his face ?

Sabu ran up the front steps, and knocked as hard as he
could, and he couldn't stop jumping up and down until
someone opened it.

' Where's the Bara Sahib ? ' he asked.   ' I must see
him.   It's very important.'   The person who had opened
the door hurried off, and the Bara Sahib came running to
the door, thinking someone must have been killed or was
ill for Sabu to be in such a fluster.   Sabu ran up to him,
and held on to his arm.

' Kind Bara Sahib, please, please and a hundred pleases,
let Irawatha come to England.'

The Bara Sahib sat down with relief ; so that was why
Sabu was so flustered.

' But didn't I tell you that he might be ? ' he said.

' No,' said Sabu, ' but might he really, really and
truly ? '

' Yes, yes, I am almost sure of it.'

' Oh, *mehrbani* ' (Indian word for ' thank you '), cried
Sabu (he had forgotten what ' thank you ' in English was in
his hurry), and he jumped down the steps, ran down the
drive, out through the gates, back to the stables, and back
to Irawatha.

' Irawatha, you are coming with me,' he cried, ' with
me to England, across so much water that even you couldn't
drink it all up.   Oh !   I'm so happy, Irawatha ! ' and he lay
and played with the elephant, hugging his trunk, and telling

The mother came and took it away

him all about England, so much, in fact, about England, that it is lucky that Irawatha couldn't understand it all, because he would have been very surprised when he got there.

XIII   THE SEA!

THERE were clothes and trunks and suitcases to be bought, and a hundred other things. Sabu was busy all day long, shopping when they were not filming him. In and out of the shops he went, with his teacher and one of the daughters of the Bara Sahib. If Sabu had bought his things alone, he would have bought a queer selection, for you see he didn't know what people wear in England. In India, they wear bright colours, and so naturally he wanted purple suits with orange ties and red shirts. Perhaps you too would like clothes like that, but I am sure that people would stare at you so much that you would soon take them all off.

At last all the preparations had been made. Sabu felt very grand and very proud in his new clothes. He had said good-bye a dozen times to all his friends, and in particular to the Jemadar, who was his greatest friend, and now he and his teacher were settled down in the train with all the filming party. There were a great many people to see them off, and really Sabu was glad when the train began to move out of the station. It was taking them to Bombay, where they would get on board the ship. Sabu watched the big clouds of smoke as they came past his window. Some of them looked like sheep and others like elephants, whilst a lot didn't look like anything at all. Oh! how he was longing to see the sea. He had never seen it before. Was

Sabu played with Irawatha's trunk

it really salty, and did it really look as if it melted into the sky ?   Did the moon and the sun really drop into it at night ?   Five hours passed, ten hours passed, twenty hours passed.   Hurrah !   Only four more hours of this chuff, chuff, chuff, and this rattle, rattle, rattle.   On and on they sped, three more hours, two more hours, one more hour.

' Look !   There's the sea ! '

Sabu had jumped up and was leaning as far as he could out of the window.   His teacher was holding on to his legs in case he fell out, and calling to him to come in.   But nothing would stir Sabu.   There it was, blue as blue could be, with little white things bobbing up and down, up and down all over the place.   Then he saw the station.   Back into the carriage he jumped and collected all his baggage. The train slowed up, and with a last grunt and a lot of squealing it stopped.   Everybody crowded out on to the platform.   Such a lot of things happened then, what with all the bustle and flurry, Sabu couldn't remember anything until he got to the ship.   He had never been so surprised in all his life as he was when he saw the ship.   It was too big to look at all at once.   It was like an enormous house with tall chimneys, and rows and rows of little round windows. They all had to climb up a gangway.   ' How does this keep floating on the water ? ' wondered Sabu.   ' Surely it must sink.'   He hoped it wouldn't do that before it got to London.   ' I must see London first,' he thought.   Sabu thoroughly explored the ship.   He looked in the cabins, the dining-room, saloons, bathrooms, engine-rooms, all over the decks, in fact everywhere.   Suddenly he came upon his teacher, who looked very distracted.

' Come, Sabu, and say good-bye to India.'   Good-bye to India ?   Sabu hadn't thought about that.   He wasn't

England would be lovely with Irawatha but not without him

going to see India again for at least another year, but he would come back, he was sure of that, so what did it matter saying good-bye ? He needn't be sad. So he went down on to the lower deck.

There were a lot of people there ; half of them he didn't know, so he wormed his way through, amongst all their long legs, until he came to a leg that looked like the Bara Sahib's. When the Bara Sahib saw Sabu he took him by the hand and led him to his cabin. They sat down and Sabu wondered what had happened to all the Bara Sahib's smiles.

' Sabu,' said the Bara Sahib, ' I have a disappointment for you. Irawatha is not coming to England after all.'

Sabu's eyes became very large and his mouth dropped open. All he could say was just a long ' Ooooooooh.'

' But,' said the Bara Sahib, ' you must remember that Irawatha will be much happier if he stays out in India. If he went to England, he would be put in a place where they keep lots of other animals and he would have to stay in his stable nearly all the time, because in an English winter it would be too cold for him to go out. He wouldn't have half such nice food as he gets in India, because in England it would be too hard to get what he likes. He wouldn't be in any more Maharajah's processions, and I expect that he wouldn't like it at all. Irawatha doesn't like going to the cinema, eating sweets, and doing all the things that you like to do, so you must remember that even though it hurts you to leave him behind, he will be much happier. Just think how nice it will be when you come back to India to find him there waiting for you, because, as you know, he could never forget you, now could he ? "

' Oh no,' said Sabu, nodding his head hard. ' But I did want Irawatha to see all the lovely things that I shall see.'

He had said good-bye to the Jemadar, his greatest friend

' Well, think of the fun you will have telling him all about everything.' That certainly sounded fun to Sabu. He would see Irawatha again and it didn't sound at all as though he would have liked living in England. Sabu decided that he must tell Irawatha why he couldn't come, and that England was not a place for elephants. Yes, if Irawatha couldn't come, it was really much better, and all of a sudden his smiles came running back, and when he and the Bara Sahib arrived back on deck, you would have thought they had been telling each other funny jokes.

Now came the good-byes. He shook hands a great many times, said good-bye a great many times, and when no one was looking he slipped off to the very back of the ship.

A hooter blew. Some bells clanged, and all of a sudden there was a distant rumble. Then the ship began slowly to move away from the docks, with a great deal of churning in the water, and people shouting everywhere. Sabu was leaving India to go to a strange land, where it was colder than India, and was full of white people. He pinched himself. Was he dreaming, was he really in a ship ? Yes, of course he must be. India was some distance away now. It was getting smaller and smaller. India, that Sabu had always thought so large, seemed to be getting really very small. He could only just see the houses, and now they were all a blur. England must be an awfully long way away, thought Sabu, if India was getting left behind so quickly, and yet they were going to go on leaving India behind for three weeks.

He could hardly see it now. It was just a little streak on the edge of the sea. How soon would it disappear ? But Sabu never found out, because his teacher called him away to lunch, and India disappeared while he ate his soup.

Good-bye to India